MW00627930

The Next CEO

A Leadership Parable...

The Next CEO

A Leadership Parable...

about values, perspectives, change, and success

By

Dr. Tommy Shavers

Visual Cover Consultant: Grace O'Connor–Photogracey.com

Published by

Commit 2 Publishing
Orlando, FL 32878

Copyright © 2013 by Tommy Shavers
All rights reserved. No part of this publication may be
reproduced or transmitted in any form or by any means,
electronic or mechanical, including photocopy, recording,
or any information storage and retrieval system, without
permission in writing from the copyright owner.

ISBN 13: 9780989941730
ISBN 10: 0989941736

Printed in the United States of America

Table of Contents

Part One: The Selection

He's your Choice

From the lens of

Sam Mueller, Founder & Chairman

I couldn't believe this was happening. I had spent so many years pouring my heart and soul into this company, and now I was supposed to place it into the hands of some stranger? To make things worse, the board outnumbered me in their desire to hire our soon-to-be-appointed interim CEO. Sal Heinrich was a majority selection by the board for the new CEO of the firm, despite no previous experience serving as a CEO. I knew you didn't need experience to be a CEO; I just wished the CEO I was hiring did. I was more than fine with leaving all of the inexperienced wannabe CEOs on the market to be swooped up by the other firms out there. I was more than fine with them running someone else's firm into the ground; just don't mess with mine. I had a hard time giving someone an entire year to play mad scientist with the firm that I'd poured my heart and soul into leading from the beginning.

As I was driving into the office to announce Sal as the new CEO to the team, I was trying extremely hard to not display my fuming disappointment. As hard as this would be, I knew I had to change my attitude—and change it quickly—because public relations people can smell a bad attitude a mile away. But I couldn't get over the fact that the only real reason we selected this guy was that the board wanted a CEO like Mr. Nash of one of our up-and-coming competitors, Mourning and Knight Communications. With the success Nash was having, choosing someone who graduated from the same university seemed in some weird way to make our board feel as if they were hiring Nash himself. *That's what happens when you have to give people decision-making power in order to run a company you founded; they take it and make stupid decisions with it!*

As I pulled up to the office building, I saw Sal walking toward the office entrance. As I made my way into the building, I noticed the front desk was unattended. I was making a mental note to fire the front desk person when I remembered that I had asked the entire office staff to meet in the company meeting room on the seventh floor for our special meeting. New mental note: "Don't fire anyone...yet." I picked up the pace to get to the elevator before it closed, not realizing until I entered that Sal was already inside it. I quickly greeted him in an attempt to hide my disapproval. "You ready, son?" I said in the most condescending, sarcastic tone I could muster. Well at least that's how it sounded in my head—not sure if it came out that way.

"Yes sir, Mr. Mueller, I'm ready; I won't let you down," Sal replied confidently.

"Oh please, don't call me sir," I said. "It's Sam, but my friends call me Mr. Mueller," I replied jokingly—well, sort of.

As the elevator was going up, I wondered to myself if I was being too hard and close- minded about this appointment. After all, Sal had performed admirably on the trial account we'd had him work on during the interviewing process. He developed the proposal, secured the account, and was lead consultant for its two month duration. During that time, he also found time to save a child from a burning building, rescue a cat from a tree, help an elderly woman across the road, and deliver a baby. Twice! At least that's how the board and the firm made it seem after his success with the trial account. OK, I admit that being a Mr. Nash look-alike wasn't the only reason they chose the guy. I guess I had blocked out that part of the evaluation process; maybe it was my old age getting to me, or maybe I was just still ticked about having to hand over the company I'd led for so long into the hands of some new guy. But I still can't shake this image of him rescuing a cat from a tree, which is making me not like him even more.

As a leader, you know you can't stay in the lead chair forever; however, that doesn't make it feel any better when it's time to leave the seat. I couldn't help feeling like I was being rejected and pushed to the side to rot away in my old age, and no one seemed to remember all I had done for this company and its people. I guess honestly, I was feeling just as upset with the group not wanting me to continue to lead the firm as I was with their selection of Sal as new interim CEO. At that moment—as it happens each time I began my personal pity parties—my inner voice of reason told me that they weren't rejecting me and leaving me to rot; they were simply ready to catch up with the other firms in terms of leadership. At times I wondered whose side this inner voice was actually on. By the way, I love my pity parties for one!

Rock-Star Arrival

From the lens of

Sam Mueller

As Sal and I walked into the meeting room, it was as if a planned coronation had begun. I had initially thought that I would mingle and socialize for a few minutes prior to commencing the meeting, but the standing applause as we walked in was actually the perfect time to ride the wave of momentum and get this thing over with. As Sal and I made our way to the front of the room, I motioned for everyone to take a seat.

"In all of my years, I have never experienced such an awesome welcome; what took you guys so long?" The place erupted with laughter, which saved me from the temptation of lying by saying I was just kidding.

It's amazing how at times real statements can make the best jokes, and your best jokes can be mistaken as awkward or serious statements. I recall consulting for a Christ-centered counseling organization run by three amazing women, and each time I would make a joke, they never laughed, but each time I made a non-joking statement about something in a serious manner, they would erupt into laughter. I told them I was giving up on making jokes with them;

13

true to form, they burst out in laughter over my non-joking statement. So now I just make non-joking statements and let others interpret them as jokes, and this way I get to tell people how I really feel and they rarely get their feelings hurt. But back to the meeting.

After saying a few words, which was the best I could do to portray approval while withholding my resentment at the same time, I stepped aside and gave Sal the floor. I watched as the room seemed to be entranced by his presence. They were hanging on every word that came from his mouth. I can remember feeling such energy when I met with the company for my first meeting and speech. It was hard seeing that experience taking place before me and to not be the one on the receiving end of such energy and support. I understand change is inevitable; however, times like these made me wonder if those who would come after me would have the same experiences that I treasured so much as a leader; were my experiences special at all? Or were they merely the perks of what everyone who holds this position will experience while holding office? I would like to think that I made a unique difference in this company, that I held a special place in the people's heart for my leadership over the years. However, watching how quickly the company had taken to Sal, I wasn't so sure that was the case anymore.

As the meeting was winding down, and Sal was making his closing remarks, I thought to myself—or better yet, I convinced myself—that it might be better to slip out before the meeting ended as to not take away from Sal's moment with the group. Truth is, I'm not sure I was ready to have people walking past me on their way to stand in line to give best wishes and encouragement to Sal. I'd been on the receiving end of that so many times, and I can tell you, it never gets old. Seeing the sincerity in people's eyes—well in the eyes of most. After leading for as long as I had, you gain the ability to see when someone is genuine and sincere or when someone is trying to get in the good graces of the head man. Nevertheless, for all the fakers, that one person you touch or inspire or challenge to be better than they are—when you see that person's eyes and know that they are going to be different when they walk out for themselves and for the company, it makes those additional 45 minutes afterwards more than worthwhile.

So I slipped out a side door prior to Sal's speech closing and headed back to my office. The walk back this time was different than all the other walks down this hallway. It was as if the hallway had become unfamiliar to me. It was as if with each step, I was being stripped of my armor; the armor of confidence and leadership I wore invisibly every day from the moment I entered this building and through the moments I traveled these hallways. In a moment of complete vulnerability, I said to myself, "What's happening to me?" By the time I made it to my office, I realized what had come over me. *Not only was I experiencing a transfer of leadership, I was also experiencing a transfer of power.* For so long, I had been the one who had led this company through the many challenges it faced and the successes it experienced. That person was not the person walking through my office door this time. *I felt powerless. I felt forgotten. I felt ordinary.*

As I sat behind my desk, a sudden sense of indignation came over me. "How is he going to lead this company?" I said out loud (luckily I had closed my door this time). I thought to myself, "I know what this company needs; I know all of the major clients personally, and I have built this company from the ground up. It makes no sense to just give it to the hands of someone who is not ready to lead the way I led this company." After a moment of brief insanity, my inner voice of wisdom interrupted my pity party again: this company has never been about me; it's always been about us, the people, the clients, our families, this city. Why in the world was I making this about me, me, me? I sat up straight in my chair and said to myself, "I will embrace this change of leadership and of power. I will discover what my new role is and how I will be able to serve this company from a different place of leadership. And I will allow Sal the freedom to lead the company the way he knows how while learning how to help him accomplish his goals." ***His being 30 years old should not negatively influence my respect for him as a leader or interim CEO.*** Besides, if I didn't give Sal a fair opportunity during this interim period, how would I ever know if he was actually the man for the job? Oh, and as my last item of business as CEO, fire my inner voice— effective immediately.

Part Two: The Friction

Ends and Means

From the lens of

Sal Heinrich, Interim CEO

In the first few months on the job, Sal closed some huge accounts but did so in a way that went against Mr. Mueller's values and principles. They had several private meetings in which they went back and forth about the issue. Sal was frustrated because he viewed Sam as haggling over red tape instead of crediting him for closing tough accounts. Sal began to think that Sam had animosity toward him because of his early success in such a short time. He also knew from an anonymous source that Sam was not thrilled with his selection as interim CEO. During these conversations, Mr. Mueller reminded Sal of his core principles: 1) principles are timeless, 2) innovative thinking is the fountain of youth, and 3) everything has a shelf life.

Business was booming! In the short time of being in charge of It's Real, Sal had scored some major victories on the competition front by winning some major accounts for the firm. Morale seemed to be at an all-time high around the building. The place was buzzing over the possibility of It's Real returning to prominence as the top dog of PR firms in the city. After reading the reports and evaluating the company's methods of closing deals under Sal, Mr. Mueller scheduled a meeting with Sal in two weeks to discuss the company's current success.

The day of the meeting had arrived, and within that time, the company had gained another major account over a rival firm. Sal brought the preliminary report for the new account with him to the meeting just in case Mr. Mueller had not yet had a chance to review the latest success the company had experienced. Sal arrived at Mr. Mueller's office ten minutes early to make an impression. "Every little bit counts with this guy," Sal thought to himself. "Don't want to give the old man any reason to rain on my parade." The receptionist told Sal that Mr. Mueller had said to send him in upon his arrival, and she motioned toward his open office door.

Sal entered the door and immediately said "Good morning, sir," to Mr. Mueller as he shook his hand. "Please call me Sam," Mr. Mueller responded. "Please have a seat, Sal. I wanted to get a chance to meet with you to discuss the latest activities concerning the company." Sal recognized pretty quickly that Mr. Mueller had not yet said congratulations or well done—or any complimentary statement for that matter—concerning the recent successes. Sal was now beginning to wonder just exactly what this meeting was all about. Mr. Mueller continued.

"This company was built on values and principles that will outlast both of our tenures here," Mr. Mueller said. "Those values and principles are what make us who we are. Without them, we are merely another firm trying to serve in the fast-paced world of carnage and competition. Three statements were key to our success: 1) principles are timeless, 2) innovation is the fountain of youth, and 3) everything has a shelf life. I wanted to touch on the first statement to our success, as it is the statement of concern for me today.

"I have witnessed and evaluated the company's most recent success under your leadership, and while many may be excited about the victories, I am concerned about the culture that's being created as a result of those victories. There were numerous protocol violations committed while securing our recent accounts. Granted, some were minor; however, some were significant. For example, you did not wait for my final signature of approval prior to engaging in final talks with some of our most recent clients. I know you may say the deals were extremely time sensitive and we had to make a move before we lost the client. However, I would say to you: do you think your group could be efficient if everyone decided themselves that business protocol was only to be followed in non-time sensitive situations? Sal, we are in the PR business; everything we do is a time-sensitive situation!"

Sal could not believe the discussion that was taking place. Never in his wildest dreams could he have imagined that this was the meeting he was so eagerly looking forward to having with Mr. Mueller. Sal thought Mr. Mueller's speech about building the company sounded like a combination of an infomercial and a Sunday school lesson. In his mind, he was thinking that it made no sense—if principles are timeless, then why would you need a fountain of youth? And if they aren't timeless, and you find the fountain, then what does it matter that things have a shelf life? You've discovered the stinking fountain, so obviously this shelf life thing is irrelevant!

Sal said to himself, "Besides, I'm bringing new approaches to the company, and it's breathing youthful life and energy into everyone in the office. At the end of the day, the question is: did we get the job done? I tried all of the red-tape 'principles' Mr. Mueller was so crazy about. All they got us was wasted time and potentially lost clients. *I couldn't afford to favor protocol over production, especially when protocol was threatening the company's performance. Maybe it's time we thought about changing protocol.* I know I can't say these things to Mr. Mueller; I'm not that stupid! I'll express my thoughts when they realize I'm too valuable for them not to name me the permanent CEO and remove this stinking interim title."

No Respect

Mr. Heinrich was addressed by Mr. Mueller again for another account issue. Sal was now beginning to think that Sam could be going senile and that he needed to step back from the hands-on approach he was taking with his leadership of the company. If Sal weren't in an interim position, he would recommend to the board that Mr. Mueller be phased out of daily operations in order to not hinder team morale and progress because it seems he always found a way to find the cloud in every silver lining!

It's Real PR was experiencing rapid morale boost, yet Mr. Mueller was concerned that the morale and the success were both inflated and not built on the values and principles he had developed. Maybe he was the one looking at this thing all wrong; maybe his practices were outdated, but would that also mean that his principles were as well? ***Are your approaches so married to your principles that in reality, the way you choose to do things begins to define what your true values and principles are?*** This was the dilemma facing Mr. Mueller; was it him as the founder not being respected, but pushed out as an old timer? Was Mr. Heinrich justified in his not adhering to the values and principles of the company with his aggressive, risk-taking approach that was producing results?

Sal's reasoning for this new account dispute was, again, that there was so much red tape and foot dragging going on that there was no way for the firm to be successful if they just stuck to old protocol. He felt that he had a choice to make in order to prove to the board and the employees that he could lead this company back to the top. He was confident in his leadership skills; however, he felt the current culture of doing business was not only setting the company up for failure but also potentially making him look like a failure as a CEO. ***Do you follow protocol and fail, or do you challenge protocol and succeed?***

This was the dilemma facing Sal as interim CEO. "But I just don't understand," Sal thought to himself. 'We're winning again; we are actually winning again, and he's complaining about me not waiting for his stinking signature or review of the contract before I closed the deal! Are you kidding me? ***How about you move faster and stop trying to force the company to move slower; and if you can't keep up, then get out of the race."*** Again, these thoughts Sal kept to himself.

After this encounter, Sal was resolved in his mind about how he would lead. "I will do my best to value the way things are done around here; however, when I feel that the values are hindering our performance, I will challenge those values until they change. ***Why***

26

hold on to values when they are outdated and are preventing your organization from growing?" Change or die.

The next day, Sal was again called into Mr. Mueller's office—and this time, things really came to a head. As Sal took a seat in the chair in front of Mr. Mueller's desk, he noticed the contract for one of the accounts the firm had recently acquired. Attached to the account folder was a copy of an email correspondence sent from Mr. Mueller to Sal. The email said the following:

> *Good morning Sal,*
>
> *This email is in regards to the potential client we are pursuing and are in direct competition with ALKconsulting. I am familiar with this potential client as well as our competition. Please be sure to stay true to our services offered and the cost for our services. For this client, there are to be no negotiations of service costs. Please contact me directly if you have any questions to discuss the matter in further detail.*
>
> *Thank you,*
>
> *Sam*

Mr. Mueller was sitting with a copy of the same document in front of him. As Sal looked at the document, he immediately knew what this meeting was about. Sal had secured the account that was sitting before him a few days ago. On this account, he recalled approving his team to work out a deal where their firm was providing service for only three of the five projects the client was developing. He had also approved a price negotiation of 20 percent lower than the company's costs for such services.

Sal sat up straight in his chair, quickly cleared his throat, and said to Mr. Mueller, "I know this may not look good on the surface, but let me explain my rationale for this deal. ALK was the client's first choice, and we were going to lose this account to them had we not found a way to bring this client on board. Just to be clear, we did not technically break protocol; we adapted to gain a new client. We did not negotiate our prices—in fact, they were not negotiating with us at all; they were telling us that they were heavily considering ALK for their services. We knew we couldn't lose such a huge client to a major competitor, so we undercut them by taking away 60 percent of the client's projects from them. In addition to this, we now have an opportunity to show this client that we can offer them the best services available head to head with ALK. I have no doubt that in the future we will retain all of their projects from ALK. However, in the meantime, we are making money and building trust; it's a win-win situation."

"Do you always find a way to make your decisions make sense to you?" asked Mr. Mueller.

"Well, no offense sir, but shouldn't all my decisions make sense to me?" Sal responded. "Otherwise, there would be no sense in me making such a decision."

Mr. Mueller seemed to have had enough at this point and said in a stern voice to Sal, "Son, all you care about is yourself and your image; you care nothing about this company or its values and principles. I gave you clear direction on how to approach this client; this was an all-or-nothing account approach. We could have had it all, but the problem was that you were too concerned with potentially leaving with nothing."

"But they were about to walk out of the meeting," Sal said.

"Then let them walk!" Sam shouted. They would have come back, or you would have left with the values of the company still intact; *we do not change the value of who we are for the value of what we want*. That's what we're about, son; we are about who we are. As much as this hurts me to say, I cannot see you as CEO material for this company."

Sal was shocked by Mr. Mueller's comments and sat there a moment to collect his thoughts on what he was going to say next. He finally responded, "Mr. Mueller, at least allow me to finish my time as CEO, and you and the board can weigh my entire body of work. I apologize for not following the directions you laid out in the email; I was merely trying to do right by the company. All I am asking is that you allow me to finish what I have started, and then you guys can make your decision." Sam agreed.

Follow the Leader

On his way home from the office, Mr. Mueller stopped by Jesse's Pizza Shop to pick up dinner. This was his favorite place to eat in the entire city. Mr. Mueller loved the food there so much so that he'd established a lunch partnership with the place—providing free lunch on Wednesdays for all the PR staffers, which is why all team meetings were held twice a month, every other Wednesday. Once inside the pizza shop, Mr. Mueller recognized that one of his company's interns was inside. This was the intern they always sent to pick up the pizza for the biweekly staff meetings and strategy meetings. Trying to hide his frustration from meeting with Sal, Mr. Mueller made a conscious effort to be upbeat and engaging with the intern. He went over to the table where he was sitting and stood next to him.

"So you're hooked on the pizza here too, huh?" Mr. Mueller said to the intern. The young man turned around and was shocked to see Mr. Mueller standing over his shoulder.

"Uh, no, sir—I mean yes, sir," the young man stuttered.

"Relax son. I must confess, the pizzas for our meetings were more for me than for anyone else; I love this place." Just then, Jesse, the owner, came from the back and greeted Mr. Mueller.

"Sammy," he said. "I see you've met my boy, Dave."

Mr. Mueller replied, "And I see you've met my intern as well." Jesse was surprised to find out that Dave was an intern at a top PR firm, and Mr. Mueller was surprised to find out that he was the son of the owner of Jesse's Pizza.

Jesse said to Dave, "You never told me you worked for Mr. Sammy, son. Had I known that, I would have charged you double every time you came in to pick up those orders!" Both Mr. Mueller and Jesse burst into laughter. Dave never talked about his internship with the PR firm because he was the one kid who was not planning on going into the family business. As a result, Dave kept all of his professional endeavors and aspirations to himself.

Dave was both embarrassed and excited in that moment— excited because he was standing in the presence of the great Sam Mueller; embarrassed because Mr. Mueller now knew that the pizza shop they sent him to for orders twice a month just so happened to be his father's business.

"How's my boy doing over there in the big corporate world, Sammy?" Jesse asked. Dave was still shocked that his dad knew Mr. Mueller well enough to actually call him Sammy!

"The kid's doing just fine," Mr. Mueller said. "If he keeps his head down, nose clean, and aspirations high, the sky's the limit for him. Well, I gotta run; take care, Jesse, and see you in the office tomorrow, Dave."

"Yes, sir, Mr. Mueller, sir!" Dave responded with embarrassing enthusiasm.

"Call me Sam," Mr. Mueller replied as he exited the door of the pizza shop. "And don't call me sir—well at least not when I'm in your dad's shop."

"Did you hear that Davie boy? One day you'll be a big timer like old Sammy there!" Jesse shouted from behind the counter to his son. *"Following a good leader usually gets you to where you wanna go,"* he added.

"Hey pops, if you insist on continuing to embarrass me in front of the customers, the least you can do is give me a 10-inch on the house," Dave shouted back to his dad.

"*Nothing in life is free, son; even the free stuff isn't free!*"

Jesse replied, laughing. "Hit those dishes in the sink in the back, and you got yourself a 10-inch just the way you like it—free!"

Part Three: The Meeting

The Client

The Valley™ was the fastest-growing company of its kind. Referring to itself as a leverage company, The Valley™ quietly made a name for itself by being a transaction and strategic leveraging corporation. They found ways to significantly improve an organization's bottom line by developing strategic partnerships within and across industries to maximize profits, increase national notoriety, and expand organization footprints in the market. A modern spin on an old practice, the services offered by The Valley™ could be somewhat defined as global market bartering or soft organizational mergers. Companies were serving companies, and industries were serving industries, with The Valley™ serving as the bartering scout, negotiator, and logistics developer. This had brought the once small business consulting group to growing national prominence as a leverage consultant corporation.

With their staggering success being widely documented, many other companies had attempted to enter the seemingly lucrative industry of leverage consulting. Once a behind-the-scenes organization, The Valley™ now recognized the need to portray an image brand to the public as the pioneer and leader in organizational/industry leverage consulting.

The founder and CEO of The Valley™, John Hale was inspired by the idea of leverage consulting during a conflict resolution session he'd had between two small business owners who were once friends and partners. During a heated time in the talks between the two small business owners, Mr. Hale threw out an unprecedented idea that had since become known as the "Hale Mary" and as the origin of the concept of leverage consulting. John suggested that instead of wasting so much time, energy, and resources fighting over such a small piece of the market pie, why didn't they put their time, energy, and resources together to grow both of their shares of the pie? He said to them, "After all, you're not in this industry to squander your money in cat fighting; you're in this industry to be successful and grow your business. Why fight each other when you can fight others together?"

John went on to address what he thought would be the next thought, which turned out to not be the next thought at all for two small business owners—for larger corporations, yes; small business owners, not so much.

He went on to say, "I know the hesitation could be: how is this not monopolizing an industry or industry collusion? Well, all you would do would be to exchange services for services; bartering or a soft merger if you will. There would be no exchange of client information except for contractual purposes; however, instead of monies being exchanged, services with monetary value are exchanged instead." John went on to state that most businesses, especially small businesses, have more untapped human capital than they have financial capital. The problem is they rarely ever leverage their human capital effectively enough to generate organizational growth. The funny thing about that initial meeting was that the two company owners stopped listening to John the moment he said the word *together*! Those two business owners never met again, nor did they retain John's services after that. Both companies were out of business within the next ten months; however, John took his inspired concept of leverage consulting and refined it over the years to what had become a new niche industry with small and large companies alike—all trying to find a way to do more without having more.

The Valley™ reached out to what they considered, through extensive research, to be the two top marketing and public relations firms in the area—and arguably two of the top firms industry wide: PGMG and It's Real PR, respectively. Both companies were called simultaneously about the potential of acquiring their services by Valley™ representatives who were both seated in the office of CEO Hale while making the calls. The company was looking for a proposal from each PR firm that would convey how each would best promote

The Valley™ to the public as the industry leader in leverage consulting. At It's Real PR, Sal personally assured Valley™ reps that he would be directly overseeing their proposal for the company and expressed tremendous appreciation for their consideration of It's Real PR. However, Sal's excitement became short lived when he was informed by the Valley™ rep that PGMG would be his direct competition for acquiring their business and that the lead consultant representing PGMG would be none other than Lionel Goldman.

The Competition

Lionel Goldman was the lead consultant for PhilGoldman's Marketing Group. Lionel's family had started PGMG many years ago, and now the great-great-grandson of the founder was the firm's lead consultant. Often in companies, employees that have the same last name as the name of the building have typically "inherited" their jobs within the company. This was not the case with Lionel. Lionel was head and shoulders above all the other PR consultants in the city—both literally and professionally. A former all-American football player and track & field javelin thrower in college, Lionel Goldman wore the jersey number 99, because as his football coach often said, "It was the closest thing they had to 100," and Lionel was the closest thing he'd ever seen to a perfect athlete. After finishing college, Lionel immediately went to work for the company. Many were shocked that he didn't pursue a professional career in either sport; however, Lionel brought the same drive and competitive nature with him into the PR industry.

Lionel became somewhat of a legend in the PR community for his ability to crush the competition and close major accounts. In fact, there were times when a local marketing firm would ask a potential client who they were competing against for their business.

If they were told PhilGoldman was the competition, the immediate follow-up question was sure to be, "Who is the lead consultant on the account? If the answer was Lionel Goldman, some marketing groups would merely withdraw their proposal because chances were slim to none that they would actually secure the account against PhilGoldman's top consultant.

However, when Sal heard PGMG was the main competition for this major client and that Lionel Goldman was serving as their lead consultant, this became the most significant account of all the recent accounts in his eyes. Not only was this the largest account financially the company ever had the opportunity of securing, but securing the account with Lionel at the helm of the competition would only cement his case for becoming permanent CEO of the company. Sal knew that despite all of his previous success, it would be this account that would define him and his short-lived time as interim CEO. ***There are times in leading when your overall body of work can be overlooked by the significance of your leadership in any given moment.*** Maximizing a significant moment can turn a poor career around, while not doing well in a significant moment can be the beginning of the end of a once-promising career. For better or for worse, Sal recognized that this was his significant moment.

The Boardroom

As the strategy team entered the boardroom to have its initial briefing on the next potential client, they were surprised to see Sal in the boardroom seated at the conference table. Some people who had been joking and laughing as they entered quickly changed their tune as they noticed their unexpected guest. Sal had never been a part of the strategic sessions up to this point. Until now, he allowed strategic meetings to be fully run by his lead consultants. When the strategy team had put a proposal together for their potential client, the lead consultants would bring it to Sal for his approval. Very rarely did he ever object because his lead consultants would meet with him before their strategy meetings, and he would tell them the approach he wanted the team to take with each proposal.

Dave the intern entered the room a few minutes later dressed in a sports coat, dress slacks, and sneakers. He was the only one allowed to wear sneakers, according to Mr. Mueller, because he was the runner for lunch orders. Dave didn't even notice Sal was in the meeting room as he came in because he went straight over to the back table to grab the lunch order sheet and headed out the door to his father's pizza shop to pick up the food. Dave was already on the phone making orders before he left the boardroom. Dave's thought was the faster he could get the lunch orders back, the more of the meetings he would be able to be a part of. He had become so efficient at handling lunch that all he would do is step out of the room, place the orders, and have the front desk text him when the delivery had arrived. Over time, Dave had positioned himself as a regular part of the strategy team. The team would be so focused on developing strategies that they never really stopped to think about Dave's participation in their meetings and thus had no objections.

As Dave stepped out of the meeting to place lunch orders, Sal made his way to the front of the room and stood in front of what the team referred to as the money board—because, as the team would say, this was where the money was made.

"Good afternoon everyone," Sal said. "I'm here because the next potential client would be the largest acquired account in our firm's rich history. I will be directly involved in this proposal process because we will need all hands on deck for this one. Our major competition for this client is PGMG and their senior lead consultant, Lionel Goldman. Lionel is well known for acquiring major accounts, and so I have no doubt he and his team will be locked in on this one. So with that said, it's time we lock in and make history with this one! As an incentive for motivation, I am offering a senior lead consultant position to anyone who is responsible for coming up with the strategic approach we will use to acquire this client."

Someone raised their hand and asked, "Sir, what if multiple people come up with the idea together?"

Sal responded, "Then I will choose the person I like the best or dislike the least, depending on who comes up with the idea." Everyone began laughing along with Sal, expecting a different answer. After the laughing subsided, a different answer never came. Sal returned to his seat at the conference table, and the two lead consultants stepped in and immediately went to work generating ideas.

Some time had passed before Dave reentered the meeting room. Unlike most days, Dave had actually had to make a quick pickup of the orders from his dad's pizza shop due to a shortage of delivery drivers that day. It was faster for Dave to pick it up himself than to wait for the next available delivery person. While returning to the meeting with the lunch orders, Dave noticed a more intense pace to the meeting than usual. Everyone was so honed in on the money board or their tablets and smartphones doing research that no one even stopped to eat their lunch.

As Dave made his lunch delivery rounds around the conference table, he heard a voice say, "These ideas will not work with this client, and they won't stack up against PGMG—start over!" Dave looked over and realized that Sal was in the meeting, and he seemed to be pretty frustrated. Dave made a conscious effort to keep quiet and to become as invisible as possible while in the room. He did not want to face the embarrassment of having Mr. Heinrich look at him after saying something and go, "What is this intern doing in here?" In order to avoid any possibility of embarrassment, Dave sat back, kept quiet, and observed.

Part Four: The Decision

Who is this Kid?

While the meeting was taking place, a call came in from the Valley™ representatives. One of the executive assistants came into the meeting room and handed a note to Sal. Moments after reading the note, Sal got up from the table and headed for the door. On his way out, he said to the entire room, "Find a way to beat PGMG, and secure this client—now!" Just before walking out, Sal turned and said, "When I return, I expect to hear a winning proposal from someone in this room."

All of a sudden, the excitement that had initially filled the room when the new job opportunity was announced was replaced with fear and despair. No one seemed to have any original ideas to throw out, or if they had any ideas, they were not brave enough to share them with the room in fear of being labeled as a horrible idea proposer. With such a label, a person can't last long or get far in public relations. It was as if the majority of the group decided that it was much safer to not throw an idea out on the floor, keeping quiet, than try to come up with the proposal idea and earn the new role as senior lead consultant.

The more the pressure and stress built up in the room, the more the creativity and originality disappeared. People were going in circles and getting nowhere. The entire group seemed intimidated by the lead competition at PGMG and scared to be the one to put their name behind any proposal to be considered. Ironically, during the biggest opportunities of their lives, the strategy team was paralyzed by fear of failure and intimidation from the competition. As Dave sat and watched, the scene became too much to bear. He could tell no one was being themselves, and as a result, they were making no progress toward a proposal. Dave had had enough.

Seeing that people seemed resolved with not winning the biggest client in the company's history, Dave said something that seemed to get everyone's attention. He asked, "Do you all realize that we could be remembered as the team who lost the biggest client in It's Real PR's history? Is that how you want to be labeled: the team who lost the biggest one ever?"

Dave's words seemed to hit home as the group began talking about how terrible it would be to be remembered as the company's biggest losers ever! But still, no one had any ideas that seemed to generate much momentum. After a few minutes of more lively discussion but no progress, one of the team members yelled, "Face it guys; there's no way we can win this one." The room became silent, as the comment seemed to suck the life out of the entire room.

After waiting to see if someone would respond, Dave stood up and said to the group, "Look guys, I'm a nobody—an intern."

Someone interrupted and shouted out, "But a good one at that!" The room erupted into laughter.

Dave continued, unfazed: "I sit in these meetings and each time, I admire the work you guys do in here. The ideas, the dialogue, the debates—I have so much respect for what you guys do and how you do it. Now if this account is so significant, and if the competition is so great, then what do you guys have to lose? You should embrace the underdog role and let it motivate you to do the unthinkable: win a client over PGMG and secure the biggest account in company history. Now I know you guys might think I'm crazy, but stay with me. How about we go totally unconventional and do something that both Valley™ and PGMG could never have seen coming? What do we have to lose as this point? Think Mike Tyson vs. Buster Douglas, David vs. Goliath, 1960 World Series, The Miracle on Ice— giants lose to underdogs because they often underestimate them."

Someone chimed in, "Except when the Giants were the actual underdogs and won Super Bowl XLII against the undefeated Patriots. Go G-Men!"

Dave happened to be a Patriots fan, so he'd intentionally left that one out, assuming no one would notice. "Yeah, that one too," he responded reluctantly.

Someone asked, *"How are we supposed to do something unconventional when conventional is all that everyone in here knows?* We just spent the last few hours stuck in conventional, so how can we do anything else when conventional is all we know?"

"We can't do it," someone said from over by the door. Everyone turned to see whose voice it was, and they were shocked to realize it was Sal. He had been standing outside the partially open door. Sal had begun to reenter the room when he overheard Dave the intern speaking to the room. He decided to stay outside and see how things would transpire. Sensing this was the right moment to reenter the conversation, Sal opened the door and said, "We can't do it—but maybe he can." Everyone's eyes quickly scanned the room to see who Sal was pointing at; to everyone's surprise, he was pointing directly at Dave.

Nothing to Lose

From the lens of

Sal Heinrich

After I pointed at the intern, I could tell my strategy team was caught off guard, as there were no responses to what I had just said. I made my way to the front of the room to give the team the latest update.

"Sit up and listen up," I said as I stood in front of the group. "Here's the latest. I've just received a call from the reps at the Valley™. They wanted to inform us that Lionel and PGMG have already submitted a proposal. They went on to say that they were extremely impressed with the proposal and were intending to proceed with signing on with PGMG. I reminded them of our professional agreement to have the opportunity to submit a proposal for their consideration as well. After a long silence, they reluctantly gave us until the end of business today to have a proposal faxed over to their office. They also reminded me how impressed they were with PGMG's proposal and that it was highly likely they had found the proposal they wanted. I responded, 'How can you know it's what you're looking for until you've had something to compare it to? You'll have our proposal by the end of the day.'

"So with that being said, we sit here with only a couple of hours to submit this proposal. We WILL submit a proposal. We have nothing to lose at this point, so let's throw something at them and see if it sticks! Now, the only way we can do what you guys are suggesting with an unconventional proposal is to let the kid take a shot at it. He's the only one in here at this point who has no conventional bias because he's never done this before. So unless anyone wants to throw the kid out of the room and come up something themselves, give the kid the floor."

I sat down at the table and immediately began thinking to myself, "What in the world am I doing? Are we really this pitiful that we have the most inexperienced person in the room spearheading the most important meeting of our careers?"

Dave responded briefly to my comments by adding, "I appreciate the opportunity, sir. Not that this means much, but I did help turn my dad's small business around when he was on the verge of being shut down by the big fast food companies in the local area. He had run the company for so long that he couldn't really see the changes that had taken place over the years. I was able to give him a different set of eyes to look at his situation. The real challenge, besides him being my dad, was that he had to trust what I was seeing because he knew he was unable to see what I could see. He trusted me, and we turned the business around, as you guys can see." He pointed to all of the lunch bags in the room that were from his dad's pizza shop. Everyone laughed in agreement.

He went on to add, *"I learned then that after looking at the same thing over a period of time, our eyes can become trained or conditioned to see things the way we've seen them the whole time.* I think it's the same in leadership and in our business. *I think I might be able to look at things through a different lens; not because I am any better, but just because my eyes have yet to become trained to see things a certain way, but they will too eventually.* So let's give it shot."

I was impressed already by the kid's presence and confidence. However, no championship was ever won at a press conference. We were still in a pretty bad place. I pulled out my pen and pad as if to take notes; immediately everyone else did the same, except with their tablets and smartphones.

I wasn't actually taking notes though; I was formulating my thoughts on how to articulate my reasoning for making such a decision to Mr. Mueller and the board. Regardless of the outcome, I knew that as CEO, I needed to be prepared with a rationale either way. My rationale would be that we knew this client was a long shot

55

to begin with. I had gathered from my initial meeting with them that they seemed more inclined to do business with PGMG from the outset. I firmly believed that our proposal was merely an unspoken formality to them. Those beliefs were strengthened by the unexpected proposal deadline and ultimatum from The Valley™, which was accompanied by their verbal expression of bias for PGMG and their proposal. So we decided to go shock and awe—to do something that at least got their attention, because getting their attention was really the only chance we had at this point at getting their business.

"Wow," I thought to myself as I continued to write. "Even I actually believe what I'm saying—impressive." My rationale would be the same if by chance the miraculous actually happened. However, I would then focus more on my leadership and talent recognition qualities as my reason for giving the intern the opportunity of a lifetime. I'll reference Saints head coach Sean Payton's onside kick call to start the second half of the Super Bowl that they would go on to win. I would then say, "Who does that?" and I would quickly respond, "A champion, that's who. A champion does that."

I was so focused on my preparation for Mr. Mueller and the board that I hadn't notice the change in the atmosphere of the room. The team was locked in and engaged with Dave's facilitation of the proposal development. I recognized that the team had picked up some momentum, and I was not going to hinder their progress. I decided to leave the room and let them finish without losing the moment. However, I sensed I could potentially be a distraction if I got up and left, as it's highly possible that a part of their confidence could be coming from my presence in the meeting. So I decided to do both: leave the room and stay at the same time, or at least attempt to. I got up to leave the room and purposefully left my notes and belongings in the room to make it seem that I was only stepping out temporarily. I decided to wait in my office and review the notes I had written while in the meeting. I had quietly taken a picture of my notes with my smartphone. I had seen some of the younger staffers do it and thought it was dumb and pointless. I still think it's dumb though—except in an extenuating circumstance, like this one.

A little under an hour had passed when one of my lead consultants came into my office. He said that the team had come up with a proposal, spearheaded by Dave. I looked at my lead consultant and asked him directly, "In your professional opinion, was this proposal the best we could do?" His reply was very calculated as he said that it was indeed unconventional and different from any other proposal we had ever done. But giving our circumstances, he believed this was our best shot at it.

"Send it over to PGMG," I said to him in another unconventional move. Normally I would've reviewed and approved the proposal, but since it was more likely that I would read it and disagree with it—or at best not understand it—I would be inclined to want to correct it to make sense to my trained, established way of thinking. The proposal was both emailed and faxed over to ensure it got to them before the deadline.

There were about 20 minutes left in the work day when my phone rang. I answered to hear my receptionist tell me the Valley™ reps were on the line. It had only been a short time since we sent the proposal over. I told her to put them through, and then I placed the call on speakerphone.

"Mr. Heinrich, this is John Hale," the caller said.

"Hello sir," I said, as if it were perfectly normal for the CEO of the company to call me personally.

"I wanted to call you and personally tell you our decision and why we went in the direction we did."

"No need, sir," I said. "We appreciated the opportunity to earn your business."

"I have to confess," John said. "I didn't think we would end up going with your company in the end."

I quickly responded, "And we're so glad you did." I immediately hit mute on the phone and startled yelling and screaming like crazy, "We did it, we did it!"

The whole time, I'd been under the impression that this was a courtesy rejection call. I had no idea we had actually won the account. "What in the world did that kid send over?" I thought to myself. My thoughts were quickly interrupted by Mr. Hale saying "Hello?" and asking if I was there. I was so excited that I'd forgotten I still had the phone on mute. I quickly un-muted the phone and said, "My apologies; trying out this new speakerphone feature for the first time," which was a true statement.

John added, "Listen, something has come up that I have to attend to, but again, congrats. I'll have my reps call you first thing in the morning to hammer out details and get the ball rolling."

"Sounds good sir," I replied. "Have a wonderful day." I hung up and immediately paged my receptionist: "Round up the strategy team and find out where the intern David Ryan is and send them all to the meeting room. Be sure the first words each of them hears from

59

you when you reach them are, 'We just made history!' Meeting starts in 15 minutes!"

Part Five: The Announcement

Words from Sam

Shortly after the closure of the big client deal, Mr. Mueller unexpectedly took ill. His health faded rapidly, and as a result, he was unable to come into the office for the next few weeks. Mr. Mueller prepared a statement letter to be read at the next company meeting, which was scheduled to be held two weeks after the close of the big client account. Sam Mueller didn't end up making it to the meeting because of his health.

Two weeks had passed, and the day for the company meeting had arrived. Everyone began to enter the room for the meeting. There was a bittersweet atmosphere in the room that morning. On the one hand, many of the employees were congratulating Dave on his recent promotion as new lead consultant for the firm. People were also congratulating Sal for spearheading and landing the biggest client in It's Real's history. Sal was also being commended for bringing Dave aboard the team. Those that had been a part of the board room meeting were still talking about how the young intern—the pizza delivery boy—had stepped up and taken down PGMG with his out-of-the-box proposal. Many had expected that today would be the day they would get word on the future direction of the company and the status of Sal as the potential next

CEO. However, with Mr. Mueller not being in attendance, most expected that such an announcement would be postponed until further notice. Either way, many reasoned that the results would speak for themselves on this one.

One of the board members stood up and greeted everyone, thanking them for their hard work and recent success on closing the biggest client in the company's history. The room erupted into cheers and whistles and shouts of "Who's real—It's Real!" The scene had quickly turned into that of a high school pep rally. After a few motions to settle down, the board member requested prayers and thoughts for the speedy recovery of Mr. Mueller. He went on to thank and recognize Sal, Dave, and the rest of the team for their work and accomplishments for the company.

He added, joking, "Dave, just make sure you're still the one going to get the pizza!"

Everyone burst into laughter and began shouting out pizza orders at Dave, as was their custom before every team meeting. Dave laughed at it himself and pretended to be frantically taking orders, as was also his custom during those meetings.

The board member then mentioned unexpectedly that although Mr. Mueller was not currently present, he had drafted a statement letter that he requested be read this morning to the company. This was really out of character for Mr. Mueller, as he never missed an opportunity to be the center of attention, nor did he take lightly the opportunity to speak to a captivated audience of his working family to encourage, challenge, or inspire them whenever necessary. Right before he began reading the letter, the board member's secretary ran over and whispered something in his ear and slipped him a folded piece of paper. The board member paused for a moment as to collect his thoughts and then proceeded with reading the letter.

Mr. Mueller began by stating that after much contemplation and prayer, he had come to a decision of the future of the company. Mr. Sal Heinrich would no longer have the title of interim CEO of It's Real PR. Many expected this move—just not without Mr. Mueller being present as he was with his initial announcement of Sal Heinrich as interim CEO. Mr. Mueller went on to say in his letter:

"As founder, I have come to the realization that in my absence, I desire to leave a legacy with this firm—the firm I started years ago with a passion for people. I wish to leave a legacy and not merely the practice of functioning on the next temporary headline. And so I, while still acting founder and chairman of It's Real PR Firm, would like to leave my legacy in this moment. I have met with the board and have their full support and approval. In a counterintuitive move, however, a move I am confident is the right move for It's Real's future, I am naming for full appointment as the next CEO of It's Real PR effective immediately, David Ryan."

It seemed as if something had sucked the air out of the room. Everyone was startled, especially Sal and Dave. Both men attempted to show no signs of emotional response in the moment, probably because they were sitting right next to each other at the front of the room. They both knew without needing to confirm it that all the eyes in the room were on them in that very moment, waiting to see how they would respond. They both sat there motionless with their eyes fixed on the board member as he continued to read Sam's letter:

"Although this decision may come as a surprise to some, I believe you can personally attest that the qualities, skills, and dedication Dave possesses are a rare combination found in some of the most influential leaders to date. I truly believe Dave's life and journey have prepared him for this very moment. They haven't prepared him to know all of the nuances of daily operations of an organization our size. No—he's not prepared for that, and he does not have the experience for that. My motto on experience has always been, '*If experience were a prerequisite for all new opportunities, then no one would ever have new opportunities.'* I believe what he is prepared to do in this moment is to lead. *There are great leaders among us, but we may never experience their potentially great contributions to the world because the world never gave them a chance to lead.*

"We are not looking to see if Dave can do what has already been done; we are projecting that he can eventually lead us into what we will do successfully in the future. That is the key to true leadership succession: not replication, but succession. Dave received unconventional, yet significant training starting from his days working under his father Jesse—a hardworking, successful small business owner. He then came to intern here at It's Real and worked closely with Sal and his team, while learning the values and culture that made our firm who we are today. His leadership potential and ability to rise to the occasion were on full display when he stepped in and led our firm in acquiring the largest client in our firm's history, while doing so in competition with the most respected and feared lead consultant in our industry to date. Because of these as well as many other indicators along the way of Dave's potential as a leader, I have great confidence that if he stays true to who he is as a unique individual and leader, our company will be in great hands as it strives to continue its legacy of having passion for people and a passion for public relations."

There was a deathly silence that was immediately followed by an eruption of cheers and a standing ovation. No one had ever even considered the notion that Dave would be the next CEO of the firm, yet at the same time, no one disagreed with Sam's observations about Dave and thus his choice of the firm's next leader. The scene in the meeting was similar to the initial meeting when Sam introduced Sal as the interim CEO. However, there was a difference: in the first meeting, the excitement seemed to be more generated by buzz and change. Back then, the company was energized by the newness of a change in leadership that they felt was refreshing and exciting. No one knew what Sal would bring to the table at that point. Even though Sal had increased production and notoriety, the company stood in cheers for Dave's appointment as the new leader of the organization. The cheers from the crowd were less of an expression of dissatisfaction with Sal's results and more of an appreciation of Dave's leadership and potential.

Dave was in shock from this announcement and had no idea what to think. He was extremely loyal to Sal as CEO and to those who were leaders throughout the company. He also had great respect for

Sam Mueller and strove to embody the principles and values Sam had laid out as the foundation of the firm.

Once the announcement had been made, Sal realized what Sam had been trying to get at all along. Mr. Mueller was not anti-emerging leadership; he was an extreme advocate for leadership succession. That's why he was so hard on Sal; it wasn't that he wanted him to fail, but he wanted to be succeeded by someone who understood the value of true succession. Sal's disregard for established leadership principles and values were accepted by others in the organization because of the success that accompanied his approaches, but not by Sam. Sam firmly believed that the right individual to run the company would be one who would have a rare combination of timeless principles, an innovative spirit, and a keen awareness of shelf life. As Mr. Mueller would always say: "Everything has a shelf life."

Sal replayed in his mind the meeting he'd had months earlier with Mr. Mueller and began looking at their conversation from a more reflective perspective. He was now realizing from this startling turn of events that the three principles Mr. Mueller preached religiously were believed by him wholeheartedly. The point Mr. Mueller was trying to drive home to Sal was that the value and principles of who you are and what you stand for should not waver or

69

change with fads and trends—or else you'll never have an identity and will only be what the clients want you to be, and thus, you will never truly be anything. Secondly, innovative thinking had to do with how we approach things—not merely staying current with the times, but being ahead of them. Innovations were not conflicting with principles from Sam's viewpoint; they were anchored by them. Mr. Mueller wanted to be sure that as the firm tried new things and challenged old ways of doing things, they would never lose sight of who they were and what they were about. Who they were was not ball and chained to how they did things; it was more like the compass to get them heading in the right direction. Sal could still hear Sam saying to him: "Everything has a shelf life."

Although Sam seemed as if he'd had a hard time being replaced as the company's leader, he knew very well that he had brought the company as far as he could take it. He knew it was time for him to place the organization into the hands of someone who would lead it into its next era as a PR firm. It was important that this individual knew and appreciated what it took to get the organization to where it was today—what it took to deliver it successfully in their hands better than it was when they first took the mantle. This meant that whoever succeeded in leading the company would need to know that in understanding shelf life, their primary responsibility was to get the organization into the hands of the next leader when they themselves had brought the organization as far as they could.

The Next CEO

After collecting himself the best he could from the recent and totally unexpected developments, Sal reached in his pocket and pulled out his phone. Sal sent a reply text message that said simply, "I'm in," and then got up and headed toward Dave, who was standing amongst a small crowd at the front of the room. As Sal approached Dave, Dave started to say, "Mr. Heinrich, I had no idea about this. You know how much I supported you and still support you as a leader and a mentor—"

Sal interrupted, "No need for an explanation, son; they've made their choice, and I've made mine. I guess now this makes us adversaries; good luck, son."

Dave was confused by Sal's comments, but before he could ask him what he meant by "adversaries," Sal had already begun weaving his way through the crowd, heading for the door. That was the last time Dave saw Sal. He found out shortly after the meeting that Sal had accepted an offer to lead a rival firm in the city. The firm had approached Sal about the opportunity during his interim time as CEO. They promised him a full appointment as their next CEO as long as he was willing to be in direct competition with the It's Real firm, which he was currently leading at that time. As CEO of a rival firm, Sal would routinely pursue the same clients as Dave and the It's Real PR firm. Dave always retained nothing but the upmost respect for Sal and correctively addressed anyone in the firm who did not do the same.

The board member who led the meeting made his way back up to the podium while the employees were talking and mingling about. Sal had already exited the room at this point, and some people were still coming up to Dave to congratulate him and express their support. The board member asked for everyone's attention and asked that they take their seats for a brief moment. Once everyone was seated, the board member went on to say, "It is with deep sadness that I stand up here and share with you that we have lost our founder, chairman and friend Samuel Mueller." The board member shared that they had gotten word of Sam's passing at the beginning of the meeting and that he'd done what he knew Sam would have wanted: place the organization and its people before himself. This was why he waited until after the first announcement to announce Sam's passing; Sam wouldn't have wanted it any other way. The board member mentioned more details would come later and made his way off the stage. While the mood had become quite somber rather quickly after the announcement of Sam Mueller's passing, it was obvious everyone was trying their best to portray a positive demeanor during an unexpected, sad moment.

Without giving it any thought, Dave made his way to the podium. He stood there for a moment to gather his thoughts, and then he began to speak.

"Mr. Mueller saw something in me that I had yet to see in myself until recently: my passion to lead others to be the best they can be. This was his gift, to see the unseen and bring it into reality. Sam was a prophet of sorts, a true visionary, and an amazing leader. He has entrusted the future of It's Real PR in our hands, and what we make of tomorrow will be determined by what we do today. So today, we will take all the time we need to reflect and honor our founder, our leader, our friend, Sam Mueller—because our tomorrow will be about valuing people and embracing our principles. Rest in peace Sam; we will all miss you."

Dave's words brought a new sense of responsibility to the moment. Everyone stood in applause for Dave's words. There were no whistles or shouts like earlier; this was more of a show of resolve to honor Sam and a display of support for Dave as new CEO. As sad as everyone was about Sam's passing, you could sense after Dave's words that people were beginning to internalize his thoughts about the company and its future. Many were hugging one another and giving pats on the shoulder and handshakes of camaraderie to each other. Words were few at this point, as everyone understood by the look in each other's eyes that today would be the driving force of their commitment to becoming the PR firm of the future.

It was expected that not much productive work was going to take place for the rest of the day as everyone dealt with the loss of Mr. Mueller. Things wrapped up about an hour later than usual as everyone was trying to find a way to make it through the rest of the work day. With the announcement of him becoming the next CEO, the sudden passing of the firm's founder, and Sal's statement and abrupt exit, Dave didn't quite know how to feel as he walked back to his new office—the one he had barely settled into as the new lead consultant. As he made his way down the hall, he could not help but see Mr. Mueller's office in front of him at the end of the hall. Mr. Mueller was so big on principles that he took his open door policy to another level. His door was always open, even when he was not in the office. Most would think this was a potential liability, but Mr. Mueller saw it as a way to build trust. He reasoned that if his door could always be open, then everyone's door could too.

And there it was—Mr. Mueller's open door. Dave just stood there in the hallway with both hands on his head, staring at the

76

empty desk in Mr. Mueller's office. Dave reflected on the encounters he'd had with Mr. Mueller and all of the gems of insight and wisdom Sam had shared with him during those small and often unplanned encounters. Then Dave began to think about his father, Jesse. He remembered what Jesse had said to him that day he ran into Mr. Mueller at the pizza shop: ***"Following a good leader usually gets you to where you want to go."*** Dave then took a deep breath and said to himself in a low voice, "I am the next CEO of It's Real PR. I am the next CEO of It's Real PR." After saying it twice to himself, he quickly opened his eyes as if an inner transformation had just taken place, took another deep breath, and said to himself in a stern, audible voice: "NO—I am not the next CEO of It's Real PR. I am *the* CEO of It's Real PR." Dave committed in that moment to make the most of his new opportunity and to do his best to validate Mr. Mueller's decision to appoint him It's Real PR's next CEO.

Decoding the Parable of *The Next CEO*

The Next CEO is a modern-day parable twist on a historic Old Testament biblical story: the story of King Saul, David, and Goliath found in 1 Samuel of the Old Testament. This monumental battle also has within its plot one of the earliest case studies of generational leadership. There is a leadership triangle, if you will, that represents three varying generations and approaches to leadership. The prophet Samuel represents the oldest generation, King Saul represents the middle or current generation, and the would-be King David represents the youngest, emerging generation.

Along the way, we see the growing conflict between the prophet Samuel and King Saul on how the nation of Israel was to be led. We also see the decisive generational collaboration between King Saul and young David. They were successful in conquering a giant new obstacle in the warrior Goliath because they worked together and did not allow their generational differences to get in the way.

We later see that when David becomes king, he does not create the David Slingshot Academy and force all of his mighty men into slingshot weaponry. We see, in fact, that his mighty men were extremely diverse. King David did not force his success or approach upon his followers, but empowered them to use the unique skills and abilities they each possessed. This was a perfect example of not letting past success become a justification for having everyone buy in to your way of doing things. *The Next CEO* was also inspired by a generational leadership presentation I developed entitled "Sword and Stones." You can find out more about this presentation at www.tommyspeak.com.

The Parable Decoder

Sam Mueller: Represented the Prophet Samuel.

Dave **Ryan**: Represented David, who would become king. Ryan means *little king*.

Sal **Heinrich**: Represented King Saul. Heinrich means *home of the king*.

It's Real PR: Represented the nation of Israel, of which Samuel was prophet and Saul and David served as kings.

Jesse: Owner of Jesse's Pizza, represented David's father, Jesse. The pizza place represented the bread and cheese Jesse had his son David deliver to his brothers during the battle against Goliath.

Phil Goldman Marketing Group: Represented the Philistine nation, which was at war against the nation of Israel.

Lionel Goldman: Represented Goliath from Gath, the champion warrior of the Philistine nation.

The client, **The Valley**™, and John **Hale**, Founder: The client represented the pivotal battle between the nation of Israel and the Philistines. The Valley™ represented the Valley of Elah (*Hale* is *Elah* spelled backwards), which was the valley where both the Philistines and the Israelites took camp for their decisive battle.

There are many other "hidden in plain sight" clues within this leadership parable. As you reread *The Next CEO*, you'll begin to recognize many of these clues with each read. I have one request of you as a reader—correction, two requests. The first request is that you share this book with someone else by encouraging them to get a copy and read it. Secondly, tell them they must read the book from cover to cover to maximize the experience. DON'T tell them the twist of the book, but wait until they have read it to discuss it with them! The following are a few leadership lessons from *The Next CEO* that I hope can start some discussions about leadership that will lead to collaborative growth for leaders of all generations.

Leadership Lessons from *The Next CEO*

Lesson One:

Leaders struggle with leaving, because leaving means not leading

Have you ever experienced as a leader being somewhere as a participant or a spectator—be it a gathering, birthday event, kids' little league practice—whatever? You're there and your leadership spider senses are going haywire because you see all the lack of organization and leadership? I know what you're thinking. First, you're thinking: "That was the longest question ever. I could have easily organized it much better." Secondly, you're thinking: "I can't help it; I could so easily show them how to run things much more easily and efficiently." Sometimes you might even struggle with just enjoying an experience because you are unconsciously assessing your experiences to see how it could be better. The point is that leading for a leader is like breathing to humans; it's second nature. Leaders begin to suffocate when they are not able to lead—young and old alike. We often make the mistake of telling young leaders to wait their turn and old leaders to hurry up and get out of the way!

The key to a healthy leadership balance is creating a culture where leaders of all ages are still able to breathe (i.e., lead). Young leaders need an environment where they can truly lead while growing in their leadership capacity and opportunities. Older leaders must also be in a place where, although their capacity to lead may have diminished (and they will, for all of us), their leadership value continues to grow. I believe organizations of all types develop leadership backlogs because older leaders, who know they still have something to offer, feel the only way to stay relevant is to stay in their current positions. There is no other place to go and still lead.

The reality is that we were all made to live and lead for a time and then leave this world. We know this truth to be self-evident because we were not made to live forever; thus our leadership was never meant to be forever. However, if we believe that principles are or can be timeless, then as leaders, we must accept the temporary nature of our time in a certain role and embrace our opportunity to leave timeless principles and values behind for those who would come after us. Let's remember that an important part of leading will always be leaving. The question for leaders of all levels to ask is this: what are we leaving behind from our leadership?

Lesson Two:

Cheers for the next leader always seem
louder than yours—leaders are sensitive

As we read with Mr. Mueller, leaders have a hard time seeing someone else getting the praise and support they once received from those they once led. A considerate leader will do his or her best to genuinely acknowledge those who have led before and express gratitude for their bringing the organization to where it stands currently. You may ask what if the leader was horrible or the state of the organization is currently horrible? My response would be to try to always place yourself in the previous leader's shoes. Ask yourself what you would like people to know about you and your efforts to lead. We know that in some cases, good leaders just get a raw deal. We also understand that being an unsuccessful leader does not mean he or she is a horrible person. As leaders, we must do our best to be mindful and to have discretion with our views of leaders who led before us, because one day someone will follow our lead as well.

Lessons Three & Four:

Different approaches to leading are driven by different values of leaders

Sal and Sam had constant clashes, not because they had different goals, but because they had distinctively different ways of accomplishing those goals. Mr. Mueller and Mr. Heinrich both wanted the same thing: great success for their organization. However, that truth was overshadowed by how different their values were. Values and principles are tricky because oftentimes, we want them to define how things should go, when in fact, they really define who we are. What I mean is often, we feel the need to project our values and principles on others because rarely do we see our values and principles as being our own; rather, we see them as the way everyone should be and the way everyone should see the world. When an organization has set values and principles established, it is not the job of those who work there to attempt to change those values, but to decide if they can embrace them as their own.

However, a very important lesson to remember is that an organization's culture is created, developed, and sustained by the people who belong to the organization. The organization itself has no life, but its life and culture come from the values and principles that

87

are lived out daily among those who are a part of the organization. If you don't want people to change the culture of your organization, then don't bring in people whose values and principles are not congruent with those who are already a part of the organizational culture. However, if you do desire to shift the culture, then don't take offense at new leaders who may value things differently than those who came before them. If you are not going to allow them to lead, then allow them to leave.

Lesson Five:

*Great leaders are good at learning from other great
leaders*

My first year as a college football player, I committed myself
to learning from teammates I thought could help me to be a better
player. One player in particular stood out to me: Jeff Fye. Jeff was one
of the smallest players on our football team, yet everyone respected
and followed him. On the field, he was once of the most physical
players on the team—off the field, one of the most laid back and
easy-going guys to be around. While many others were fighting hard
for respect and attention, Jeff simply led. He didn't involve himself
with every situation, just those he felt were important to the
direction of the football team. I became Jeff's understudy.

My wife and I moved into the same apartment complex as
Jeff so I could ride back and forth to football practice with him. Those
rides were invaluable to my growth as a football player and as a
leader. We would talk about practice, what I could do better, why he
handled a situation or player the way he did, and how my progress
was going. For two years I learned from Jeff, and when time came for
the team to select our captain during his senior year, it was no
question who I voted for and who the team wanted to follow; Jeff

was voted our team leader. However, what I did not expect was that the following year, the team would select me for the same honor and responsibility it bestowed upon Jeff a year prior; I was chosen as team captain my senior year as well. I had not expected this; however, when I looked back on it, I realized that my teammates were merely acknowledging the leadership qualities I had shown over the years. Many of those leadership qualities, however, I had learned over the years from listening to, observing, and learning from Jeff Fye. I became a good leader in large part because I learned from a good leader in Jeff. Dave's dad told him that following good leaders usually takes you to good places. As leaders, it is important for us to be intentional in our learning from others whom we see exemplify the qualities and values we believe are important to our success as leaders. Thanks Jeff!

Lesson Six:

Great leaders can see what they can't see

Ever heard of the Dunning-Kruger Effect (DKE)? I first heard of it because it was the name of one of the teams in my fantasy football league: the Orlando Fantasy Football League. The second time I heard of the DKE was from one of my public speaking students I had in class who did a presentation on it. In short, DKE is when someone who is unskilled in a particular area overestimates their ability because of their inability to recognize their shortcomings. In other words, DKE is when you don't know what you don't know. I strongly believe many leaders today suffer from DKE, and as a result, confidently lead out of their incompetence. Sal, although the top organizational leader, recognized the inability of his team (himself included) to create a counterintuitive strategy proposal because they were accustomed to thinking about proposals and strategies the same way for so long.

Sometimes we can get so focused on our success that we can become ignorant to the changing world around us. Current success can often become the primary reason for future failure, as leaders can begin to think they know how to be successful in the future because of the success in their past. A great leader knows what they don't know and can see what they can't see. They are just as clear about their limitations, biases, and shortcomings as they are their strengths and talents. When we recognize our blind spots and limitations, we seek out and empower individuals who have the qualities we lack, which are critical to our overall success. When we find these individuals, however, the most important thing is that we allow them to lead in the areas they—not we—know best. When those individuals are allowed to be great at what they do, everyone benefits; when leaders suffer from DKE and believe they can do what they really can't, everyone suffers.

Last Lesson:

Experience is potential given a chance

If experience were a prerequisite for opportunities, opportunities would not exist. Mr. Mueller saw something in Dave that his resume couldn't convey; he saw a great leader who had all the intangibles to successfully lead a major organization. The only thing Dave was missing was experience leading a major organization, or even a small one for that matter. Initially Mr. Mueller expressed concern about his interim CEO's lack of experience; however, he would overlook Dave's lack of experience because of his great leadership potential. Think back to your very first legitimate job or back to how your career started. Many of us would say it was not what we knew but who we knew or who knew of us. Most of us would say that someone gave us a chance or an opportunity to do a job that when we look back on it, we admit to barely—if at all—being qualified for. The next great leader will need someone to give him or her a chance to lead. Some people today evaluate talent by looking at what someone has done previously as justification that they can do it again (i.e., relying on experience). But what if they have never had the chance to do something before? How will you know if they can be successful if given the opportunity? How risky is it to be the first to take a chance on an unproven commodity?

These are real questions facing leaders who have to balance the importance of both experience and potential in discovering emerging leaders. I don't have the answer to this one; however, I can leave you with food for thought. When choosing someone with experience, they usually give you what you expected—nothing more. A known commodity is a low-risk, low-reward situation. If you are not in a position to take risks and the threat of failure is more significant than the potential for success (as is the case sometimes), you may go with experience. However, if you desire something greater than what you know the usual suspects can deliver, and your potential for success is greater than the threat of failure, then you have to consider the high-risk, high-reward scenario of a leader with great potential who just needs to be given a chance.

Thank you for taking the time to read *The Next CEO*.

Until the next one…blessings to you and yours!

Tommy

About Tommy

Dr. Tommy Shavers is a speaker, author, minister, and former Christian radio show host. He is president and co-founder of *Unus Solutions, Inc. and Tommy Speak LLC.* Tommy also serves as a contributing author for Linked2Leadership, one of the nation's top leadership blogs. He is a former athlete, teacher, and coach. He holds a bachelor's in Organizational Communication, a master's in both Interpersonal Communication and Biblical Studies, and a Doctorate of Management in Organizational Leadership. Tommy is a USA Track & Field Level 1 Certified Coach and a member of the National Speakers Association (NSA). He has a passion for leadership and personal development and loves to see people work together to make a greater difference in the world.

Other books by Tommy:

Christ In You: The Revealed Mystery of the Power of God (Spring 2014)
None of the Above: The Power & Pitfalls of Worship (2013)
Life in the Trenches: Joys and Challenges of Christians in Sports (2004 & 2011)

Dr. Tommy Shavers
www.tommyspeak.com
www.unussolutions.com
www.trueriverministries.com

28533812R00056

Made in the USA
Charleston, SC
15 April 2014